Little Wizard
Maths 4

Lynn Huggins-Cooper

In a cave, in a magical land, far, far away lives a little wizard, called Pointy. Pointy is learning magical English powers from the great Wizard Whimstaff. He is lonely though, and would like to have a friend to learn with him. He has chosen you! Also in the cave lives Miss Snufflebeam, Wizard Whimstaff's pet dragon. She is very silly and clumsy and gets confused a lot. Then there are Pointy's two naughty pet frogs, Mugly and Bugly. What they like to do most of all is to sit around eating and croaking and burping. Sometimes they help Wizard Whimstaff with his spells though. Maybe, if you do these magical exercises, you can earn all the ingredients to do a spell of your own!

Contents

2   Ticklish 20!
4   Nice numbers
6   That is an order!
8   Flies everywhere!
10 Terrific 2s!
12 Tremendous 10s!
14 Wizarding fun
16 Pretty pairs

18 Clever counting on
20 Smashing shapes
22 Cool counting back
24 Place your orders!
26 Tellling the time
28 Wizarding fun
30 Answers
32 My first little wizard spell

Ticklish 20!

Hello! I am Miss Snufflebeam, Wizard Whimstaff's pet dragon. I was playing with these numbers and they started to giggle, because they are ticklish!

0 1 2 3 4 5 6 7 8 9 10 11 12 13 14 15 16 17 18 19 20

Help me to catch the numbers before Wizard Whimstaff sees! Write them in order in this bag.

0 1 2 3 4 5 6 7 8 9 10 11 12 13 14 15 16 17 18 19 20

2 Gosh! Thanks! Remind me what some of the numbers look like. I forget so easily! Draw a circle round these numbers on the numberline.

a 14   **b** 20   **c** 16   **d** 11   **e** 19   **f** 13

☆ 1 2 3 4 5 6 7 8 9 10

☆ 11 12 13 14 15 16 17 18 19 20

Little wizard's work

You are clever! Now circle the missing number from each group.

a | 11 12 ? 14 | missing number: 2 3 13

b | 17 ? 19 20 | missing number: 8 18 10

c | 14 15 ? 17 | missing number: 6 16 11

Burp! Well done, cleverclogs! Collect a snowflake sticker to put in your cauldron at the back of the book!

PARENT'S NOTE: *This activity will help your child to recognise the numbers from 0–20. It builds on prior knowledge gained with numbers 0–5, then 0–10.*

Nice numbers

Hello! I am Wizard Whimstaff. I have been showing Miss Snufflebeam how to write the numbers from 0–20.

1 Help Miss Snufflebeam. Write these numbers.

0 1 2 3 4 5

6 7 8 9 10

11 12 13 14 15

16 17 18 19 20

Excellent! Now copy these numbers into the boxes. I am sure you can do it!

1 2 3 4 5 6 7 8 9 10
11 12 13 14 15 16 17 18 19 20

Little wizard's work
Just check you can remember. Fill in the missing numbers.

1 2 3 4 5 6 7 [ ] 9 10

11 [ ] 13 14 [ ] 16 [ ] 18 19 20

You are clever! Add a *feather* sticker to your cauldron at the back of the book.

PARENT'S NOTE: *This activity promotes the correct formation of numerals. Give your child lots of opportunities to practise and to see you writing numbers.*

5

That is an order!

Hello there! I am Pointy, Wizard Whimstaff's assistant. I am trying to put things in order, from 1st to 5th.

1st 2nd 3rd 4th 5th

1 I found the 5th thing in the line by counting along to five. Answer these questions by colouring in the boxes the correct colours.

a What colour is the 3rd bottle?

b What colour is the 5th bottle?

c What colour is the 1st bottle?

d What colour is the 2nd bottle?

2 Super! Now draw a line of flowers.
Colour them like this.

a 1st red

b 2nd blue

c 3rd green

d 4th yellow

e 5th pink

Little wizard's work

Look at this photo of the wizard races. Was Wizard Whimstaff 1st, 2nd or 3rd?

FINISH

Well done, young wizard! Put a rose petal sticker in your cauldron at the back of the book!

PARENT'S NOTE: This activity is designed to introduce your child to ordinal numbers. Set up 'teddy races' to practise the different positions.

Flies everywhere!

Help! We opened our lunchboxes and all the flies flew out!

1 Count the flies in each cloud. Write the answer in the box. Burp!

a

d

b

e

c

f

2 Croak! That was quick! Now make us some fly pie! Draw the right number of flies in each pie.

a

11 flies

c

13 flies

b

14 flies

d

16 flies

Little wizard's work

Slurp! Delicious! Just check – draw a circle round the slug sandwich that has 11 slugs in it.

Super! Add a puff of smoke to your cauldron!

Terrific 2s!

I am counting my bricks. Wizard Whimstaff said it would be quicker if I counted in 2s.

| 2 | 4 | 6 | 8 | 10 | 12 | 14 | 16 | 18 | 20 |

1 Fill in the missing numbers to help me to count in 2s.

a 2 4 6 ☐ ☐ 12 ☐

b 8 10 ☐ ☐ ☐ 18

c 6 8 ☐ ☐ ☐ 16

d 10 12 ☐ ☐ ☐ 20

e 4 6 ☐ ☐ 12 ☐

f 10 ☐ 14 ☐ 18 ☐

2 Oh, well done! Now, how many bricks are there? Count in 2s to find the answer.

a

c

b

d

Little wizard's work

Fill in the chart for me. I will put it on my bedroom wall to remind me.

0	2									20

Croak! Good work! Add some stardust to your cauldron!

PARENT'S NOTE: During the reception year at school, children begin to learn to count in 2s. Practise by counting pairs of shoes or gloves!

Tremendous 10s!

Hello there! I am sorting things into boxes. I like to keep things tidy! To make the counting quicker, I am counting in 10s. Have you noticed that all the numbers end in 0?

| 10 | 20 | 30 | 40 | 50 | 60 | 70 | 80 | 90 | 100 |

1 Draw a circle round all the numbers that end in 0.

10

99

30

12

44

0

50

15

20

70

80

61

2 Super! Now count these stars before I put them away. Count in 10s. Each time you count 10, draw a circle round the group.

a ☆ ☆ ☆ ☆ ☆ ☆ ☆ ☆ ☆ ☆

b ☆ ☆ ☆ ☆ ☆ ☆ ☆ ☆ ☆ ☆
☆ ☆ ☆ ☆ ☆ ☆ ☆ ☆ ☆ ☆
☆ ☆ ☆ ☆ ☆ ☆ ☆ ☆ ☆ ☆

c ☆ ☆ ☆ ☆ ☆ ☆ ☆ ☆ ☆ ☆
☆ ☆ ☆ ☆ ☆ ☆ ☆ ☆ ☆ ☆

Little wizard's work
Well done! Now fill in the missing numbers.

0 10 ⭐ 30 ⭐ 50 ⭐ 70 80 ⭐ 100

Well done, young wizard! Add an eyelash to your cauldron!

PARENT'S NOTE: *Counting in 10s is a strategy to make counting large numbers easier and quicker. Practise with coins, sweets, grapes etc. Encourage your child to group together each set of ten before counting in 10s to find the total.*

Wizarding fun

Colour the shapes showing numbers that are on the 2s or 10s numberlines to find the mystery picture.

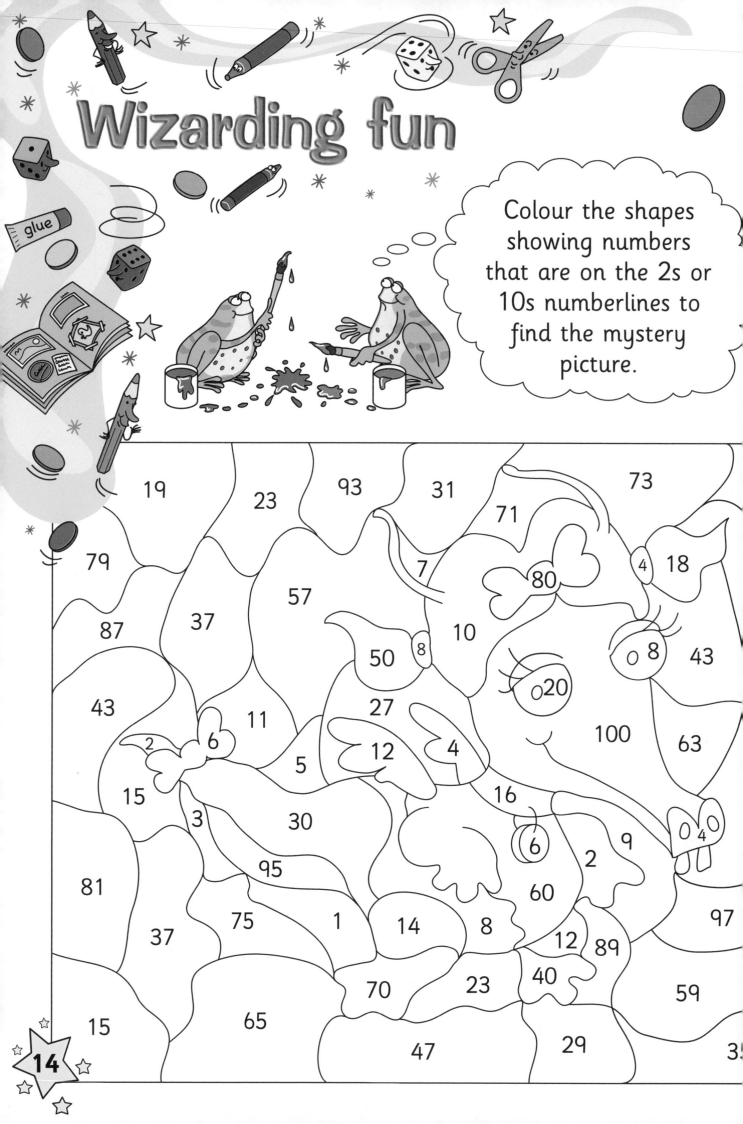

19 23 93 31 73
71
79 7 80 4 18
57
87 10
37 8 8 43
50
20
43 11 27 100 63
2 6 12 4
5
15 16
3 30
6 9
95 2 4
81 60
75 1 14 8 97
37 12 89
40
70 23 59
15 65 29
47 3

14

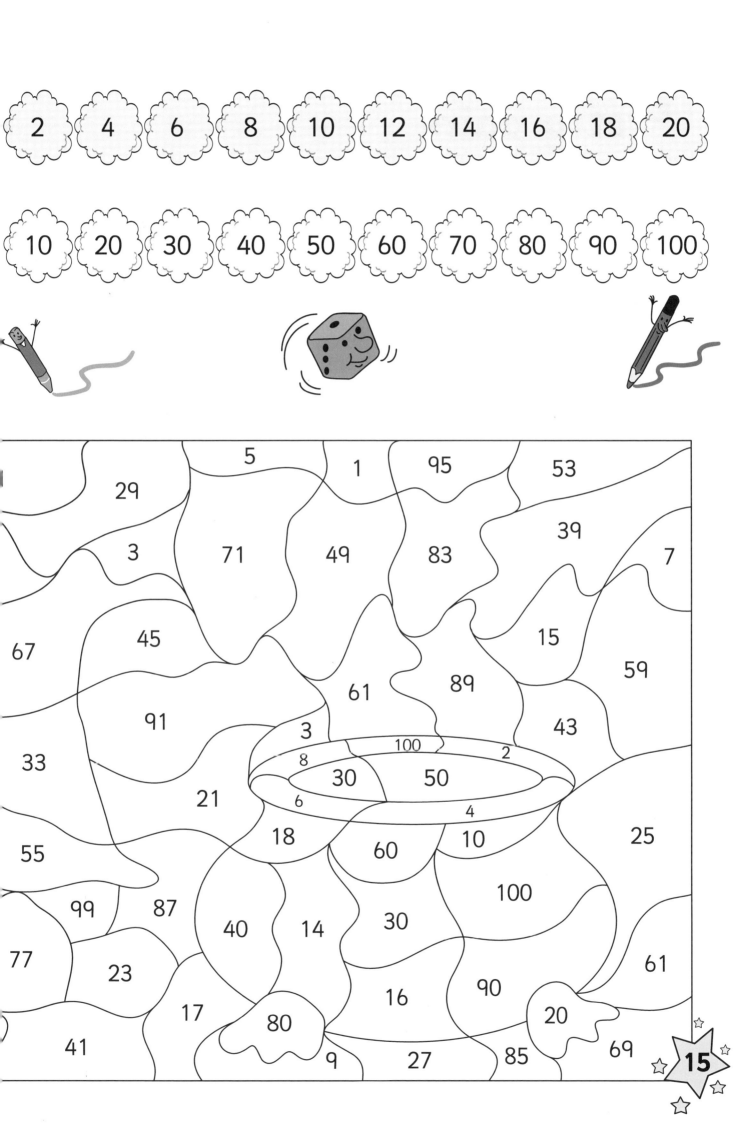

15

Pretty pairs

Burp! We are a pair, because there are two of us! We are looking at number pairs that add together to make 10.

1 Croak! Match the numbers to their partner to make 10. Join them with a line.

a 1
b 2
c 3
d 4
e 5
f 0

8
9
5
10
6
7

Cauldron Stickers

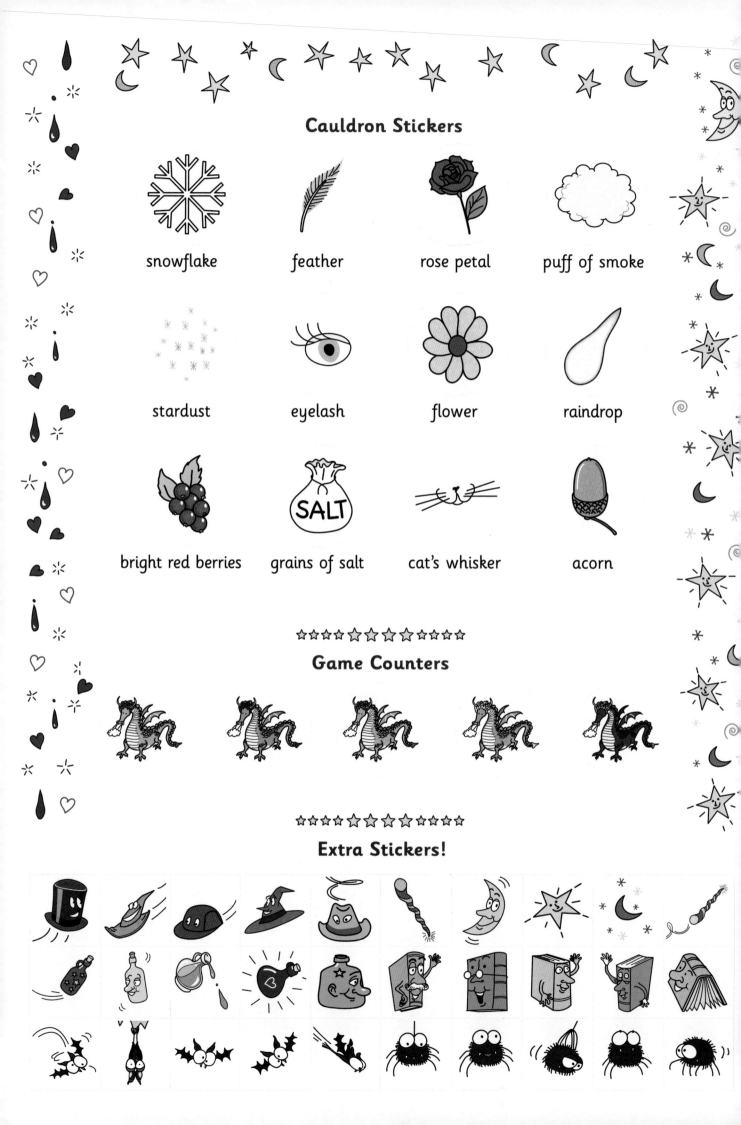

snowflake

feather

rose petal

puff of smoke

stardust

eyelash

flower

raindrop

bright red berries

grains of salt

cat's whisker

acorn

Game Counters

Extra Stickers!

2 Slurp! Now write the missing numbers on the cards. Remember, each pair has to make a total of 10.

a 3 [ ]   b 9 [ ]   c 5 [ ]

d 7 [ ]   e 2 [ ]

Little wizard's work

Now circle the numbers in each group so the pairs make 10.

a ⟨7⟩ 6 3 2   c ⟨9⟩ 2 0 1

b ⟨4⟩ 6 4 1   d ⟨1⟩ 6 9 2

Oh, you are so clever! Add a flower to your cauldron!

PARENT'S NOTE: This activity is about number bonds to 10. Learning these 'maths facts' will help your child with mental arithmetic and calculations.

Clever counting on

Hello! When I do sums, I use a numberline to count on.

$$2 + 6 = 8$$

0 1 2 3 4 5 6 7 8 9 10 11 12 13 14 15 16 17 18 19 20

1 Help me do these sums. Count on to find the totals.

0 1 2 3 4 5 6 7 8 9 10 11 12 13 14 15 16 17 18 19 20

a   4 + 5 =

d   10 + 7 =

b   6 + 8 =

e   5 + 2 =

c   3 + 9 =

2 Oh, well done! Now count on using your fingers to do these sums.

a   3 + 4 =

d   6 + 3 =

b   5 + 4 =

e   2 + 6 =

c   8 + 2 =

Little wizard's work

Abracababa! You are very clever. Can you answer these questions? How many do you count on to get from:

a   3 to 8   c   6 to 10

b   4 to 9   d   3 to 7

Excellent work! Add a raindrop to your cauldron!

Smashing shapes

Hello there! I am making a picture from shapes for my bedroom wall.

square

triangle

circle

rectangle

1 Look at the picture and count how many of each shape there are.

a

b

c

d

2 Super! Look at these three shapes:

cube   sphere   pyramid

Now look at the shapes below. Colour the cubes blue, the spheres red and the pyramids yellow.

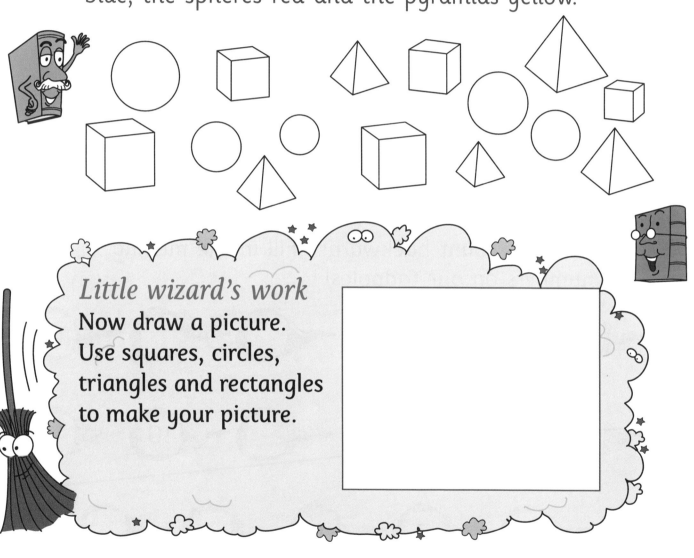

Little wizard's work
Now draw a picture. Use squares, circles, triangles and rectangles to make your picture.

That was great! Croak! Add some bright red berries to your cauldron!

PARENT'S NOTE: Look at shapes in the environment with your child. Talk about the shapes you can see in buildings, on signs etc.

21

Cool counting back

We like jumping backwards – it is so much fun!

1 Can you count backwards? Fill in the missing numbers on our tadpoles!

20 ◯ 18 ◯ ◯ 15

14 ◯ ◯ ◯ 10 ◯

◯ 7 6 ◯ ◯

3 ◯ 1 ◯

2 Burp! We like hopping along numberlines! Help us to work out the answers. Count back along the numberline.

0 1 2 3 4 5 6 7 8 9 10

a 4 – 2 = ☐

b 8 – 5 = ☐

c 9 – 3 = ☐

d 10 – 7 = ☐

e 5 – 4 = ☐

Little wizard's work

Croak! Well done! Just to check you can count back, use your fingers to find the answers.

a 10 – 3 = ☐

b 9 – 7 = ☐

c 8 – 4 = ☐

d 6 – 5 = ☐

Well done, young wizard! Add some grains of salt to your cauldron!

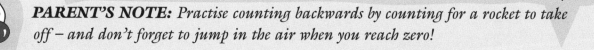

Place your orders!

I am playing teddy races. I have made some rosettes for my teddies.

 1 Look at the teddies and answer the questions. Colour the box to give your answer.

a What colour is the 5th teddy? ☐

c What colour is the 10th teddy? ☐

b What colour is the 2nd teddy? ☐

d What colour is the 7th teddy? ☐

2 You are clever! Now draw a line of 10 hats. Colour them like this:

1st green

2nd red

3rd blue

4th purple

5th orange

6th pink

7th grey

8th black

9th yellow

10th brown

Little wizard's work
Abracababa! You are very good at this! Just check you remember. This teddy won the race. Write the number it should have on its rosette.

Super! Add a cat's whisker to your cauldron!

PARENT'S NOTE: Ordinal numbers are a difficult concept. Help your child by staging 'toy races', making badges for the competitors.

Telling the time

3 o'clock

I like to tell the time. It helps me to get all my jobs done! I like o'clock time best, when the big hand points straight up, to the 12.

1 Look at these clocks. Tick the right time for each clock.

a   b   c   d

☐ 3 o'clock	☐ 10 o'clock	☐ 7 o'clock	☐ 6 o'clock
☐ 2 o'clock	☐ 9 o'clock	☐ 12 o'clock	☐ 2 o'clock
☐ 1 o'clock	☐ 11 o'clock	☐ 8 o'clock	☐ 8 o'clock

2 Excellent! Now draw the hands on the clocks to show the time. Remember, with **o'clock** the big hand always points to the 12.

a

3 o'clock

b

9 o'clock

c

12 o'clock

d

1 o'clock

e

7 o'clock

Little wizard's work

Super! Now write the times you see on these clocks.

a I have my breakfast at [ ] o'clock

b I have my dinner at [ ] o'clock

Slurp! Well done, cleverclogs! Add an acorn to your cauldron!

PARENT'S NOTE: *Learning to tell the time – takes time! Start with o'clock time, then work on half past, quarter to and quarter past. Use a toy clock to help your child to learn.*

Instructions:
You need some scrap card, scissors and a dice. Stick the five dragon stickers in the back of your book onto some scrap card and cut them out. They are your counters.

How to play:
Use a dice to see how many spaces each dragon moves on each turn. Carry on until all the dragons have reached the treasure. Then draw the dragons in the right place to show where they finished in the race.

Answers

Pages 2–3

1 Numbers 0–20 written in order in the bag.

2

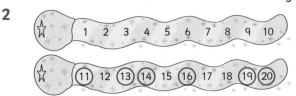

Little wizard's work
- **a** 13
- **b** 18
- **c** 16

Pages 4–5

1 Numbers traced correctly.

2 Numbers 1 to 20 copied correctly in order in the boxes.

Little wizard's work
Numbers 8, 12, 15 and 17 written in the spaces.

Pages 6–7

1 **a** yellow   **c** orange
  b blue   **d** green

2 A line of flowers drawn with the first being red, the second blue, third green, fourth yellow and the fifth pink.

Little wizard's work
1st

Pages 8–9

1 **a** 12   **d** 17
  b 16   **e** 19
  c 11   **f** 18

2 **a** 11 flies drawn in the pie.
  b 14 flies drawn in the pie.
  c 13 flies drawn in the pie.
  d 16 flies drawn in the pie.

Little wizard's work

Pages 10–11

1 **a** 8, 10, 14   **d** 14, 16, 18
  b 12, 14, 16   **e** 8, 10, 14
  c 10, 12, 14   **f** 12, 16, 20

2 **a** 10   **c** 12
  b 14   **d** 16

Little wizard's work
Numbers 4, 6, 8, 10, 12, 14, 16, 18 filled in on the number chart in that order.

Pages 12–13

1

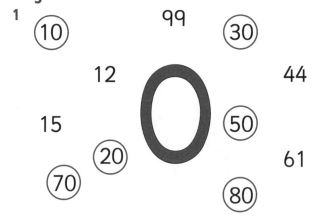

2 **a**

b

c

Little wizard's work
Stars filled in with 20, 40, 60 and 90.

30

Pages 14–15

All numbers which are divisible by 2 and 10 coloured in, revealing Miss Snufflebeam and a cauldron.

Pages 16–17

1
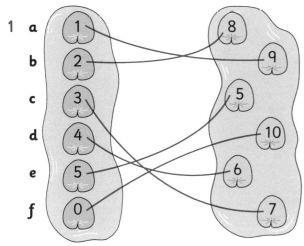

a 1
b 2
c 3
d 4
e 5
f 0

8
9
5
10
6
7

2 **a** 7   **b** 1   **c** 5
   d 3   **e** 8

Little wizard's work

a 7   6 ③ 2

b 4   ⑥ 4 1

c 9   2 0 ①

d 1   6 ⑨ 2

Pages 18–19

1 **a** 9   **d** 17
   b 14   **e** 7
   c 12
2 **a** 7   **d** 9
   b 9   **e** 8
   c 10

Little wizard's work

a 5   **c** 4
b 5   **d** 4

Pages 20–21

1 **a** 3   **c** 2
   b 9   **d** 9

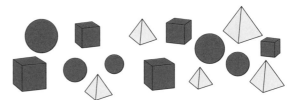

2

Little wizard's work

A drawing made up of squares, circles, triangles and rectangles.

Pages 22–23

1 Numbers written in tadpoles as follows
   19, 17, 16, 13, 12, 11, 9, 8, 5, 4, 2, 0.
2 **a** 2   **d** 3
   b 3   **e** 1
   c 6

Little wizard's work

a 7   **c** 4
b 2   **d** 1

Pages 24–25

1 **a** blue   **c** green
   b red   **d** orange
2 Ten hats drawn and coloured as described.

Little wizard's work

1st

Pages 26–27

1 **a** 2 o'clock   **c** 12 o'clock
   b 10 o'clock   **d** 8 o'clock
2 **a**   **b**   **c**

   d   **e**

Little wizard's work

a 8 o'clock   **b** 7 o'clock

31

My first little wizard spell, by ——————————.

Published 2006

Letts Educational, The Chiswick Centre,
414 Chiswick High Road, London W4 5TF
Tel 020 8996 3333   Fax 020 8742 8390
Email mail@lettsed.co.uk
www.Letts-SuccessZone.com

Text, design and illustrations © Letts Educational Ltd 2002

Author: Lynn Huggins-Cooper
Book Concept and Development: Helen Jacobs, Publishing Director
Project Editor: Lily Morgan
Design and Editorial: 2idesign ltd, Cambridge
Cover Design: 2idesign ltd, Cambridge
Illustrations: Andy Roberts
Cover Illustration: Andy Roberts

Letts Educational Limited is a division of Granada Learning Limited.
Part of Granada plc.

British Library Cataloguing in Publication Data

A CIP record for this book is available from the British Library.

ISBN 1-84315-626-1

Printed and bound in Italy.

Colour reproduction by PDQ Repro Limited, Bungay, Suffolk.